THIS BOOK BELONGS TO:

NAME:

ADDRESS:

CONTENTS

iMouse

WINTER SPORTS

These two pictures might look the same, but if you look carefully you should be able to see 10 small differences. Can you spot them all?

Answers: The 10 differences are 1. snowman's hat 2. missing cloud 3. missing bird 4. Spike's teeth 5. missing

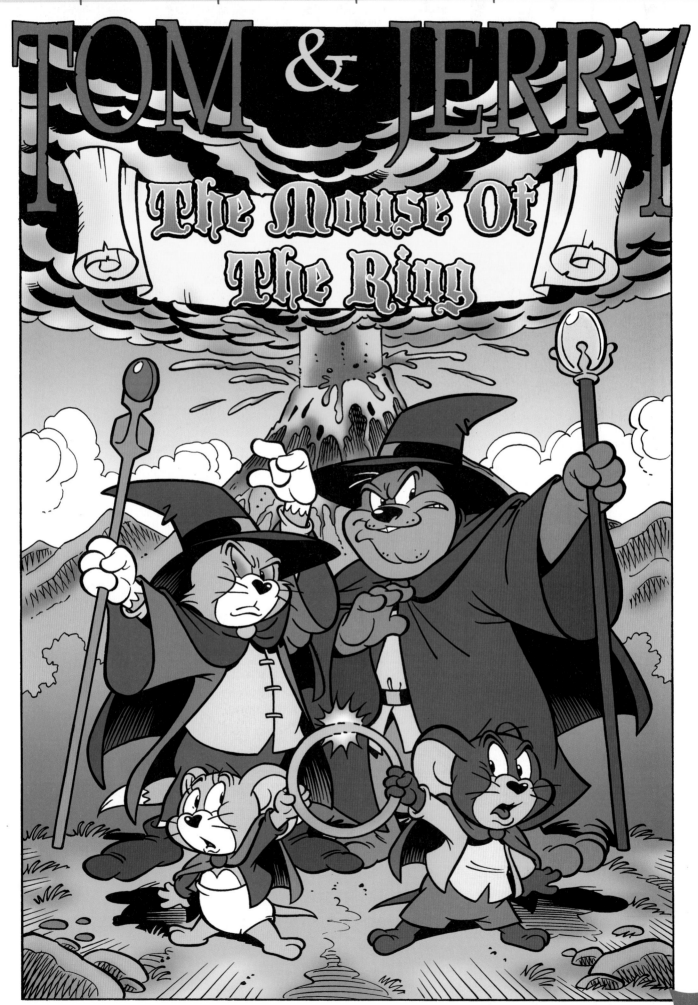

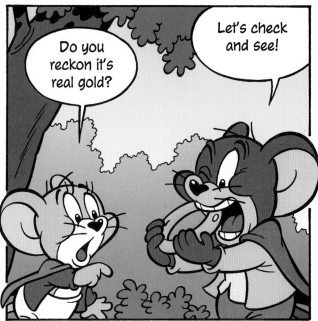

It works! The ring's doing its thing again!

Look! The ring is granting your wish. It can read your mind!

Huh? Are you sure that's what you wished for?

I'm sorry, but I really need to go...big time!

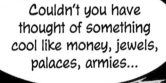

Couldn't you have thought of something cool like money, jewels, palaces, armies...

Why are you pulling that weird face?

With this ring we could have anything! We could rule the world! Bwa-ha-ha-ha-ha!

THWAK!

Continued on page 14...

11

MAKE YOUR OWN SOCK PUPPIES

You can have lots of fun with these cool sock puppet puppies!

You will need:: old socks, scraps of material, card, safe glue or a needle and thread.

Ask a grown-up for an old sock. Put your fingers in the toe and your thumb in the heel!

2

Use long strips of scrap material for your puppy's floppy ears or you can cut out triangles of card if you want to make a kitten. Use smaller scraps of material for the nose and eyes. You can stick them on with safe glue or get a grown-up to stitch them on.

Always take care when using scissors or sharp objects. Ask a grown-up for help!

Continued from page 11

The ring was created by an evil wizard to increase his own power. It's a magic ring, forged in the lava of Mount Creepy, the world's most dangerous volcano!

It rolled and rolled for days and days...

But the ring's energy was so great that one day a great thunder storm filled the skies. A lightning bolt struck the ring from the wizard's hand!

Since then, many evil wizards have hunted for the ring!

They want to use it's power to rule the world. The Wizard Tom is the worst of all!

If he finds the ring then he will rule us all!

Continued on page 19…

17

draw and colour... draw and colour, draw and colour, draw and co

STOCKING FILLER

It's Christmas morning and Jerry is about to open his presents from Santa. Can you draw his stocking in the empty space?

Continued from page 17

Gotcha!

What's that thing you've just caught, little mouse?

It looked just like a ring to me? Am I right or am I wrong? Do tell!

Oh no, it's Wizard Tom!

We haven't got anything. Look!

Glub!

Hmmm! I smell a rat!

Continued on page 28...

LET'S GO FLY A KITE

Join the dots from 1 to 4 and then use your crayons to draw a nice pattern on Tom's kite!

WELCOME TO PANTO

LAND

ZZZZZ!

Can you spot all these pantomime characters in the picture?

Sleeping Beauty

Snow White

Wicked Witch

Seven dwarfs

Cinderella

The Ugly Sisters

Prince Charming

Jack and the Beanstalk

The Giant

Buttons

Puss in Boots

Fairy Godmother

TOM & JERRY

The Mouse Of The Ring
Part 2

The rest of this mission is just like a pleasant stroll in the woods!

Yeah! No more danger! We've got nothing to be scared of anymore!

OSCAR MARTIN

Nothing's going to bother us now! We can just relax!

Continued on page 35...

WHAT'S ON THE MENU?

Tom and Jerry are preparing their Christmas dinner. Can you fit all of the foody names into the grid?

- ☐ roast potatoes
- ☐ mince pies
- ☐ Christmas cake
- ☐ stuffing
- ☐ turkey
- ☐ cream
- ☐ gravy
- ☐ carrots

Unscramble these words to find Tom and Jerry's favourite food.

shif   **eschee**

Who likes which food?

Answers: fish, cheese

31

JOURNEY TO MOUNT CREEPY

START

1

2

3 Hide from Wizard Tom's army miss a turn.

4

18 Caught in spider's web. Miss a turn.

19

20

13

14

15 Get lost in fog. Go back to 9.

16

12 Tree people stand on you. Miss a turn.

11

10 Fly to 13.

9

8 Battle with Spike the Wise. Go back to 5.

7

You can be either Wizard Tom or Jerry in this race to the volcano. You will need two counters and a coin. When it's your turn to move flip the coin, if it is heads you move forward two spaces, if it is tails you move forward one space and obey the instructions on the rock. The first player to reach the volcano wins the game. Good luck!

Continued from page 30 →

BONK!

Jerry, Tuffy, run now! Escape while you can! Don't stop until you reach the volcano!

Do we really have to go to the volcano? Couldn't we just try melting the ring with a match?

I don't think that will work, Tuffy!

I was afraid you would say that!

We've been running for ages and this ring weighs a ton. I'm shattered!

Can't we rest for a bit? It's dark and... pant...pant!

Yeah! Let's sleep for a bit. We've gotta be out of danger now!

37

All I could do was live for the ring and little by little it changed me.

My lovely treasure!

It turned me into a monster. Then one day I lost it!

I don't want that to happen to me! I'm not going to turn into a monster!

My treasure! It's mine again!

No! Keep away from that ring!

Oooofff!

Grab the ring! We've got to complete our mission!

Give it back!

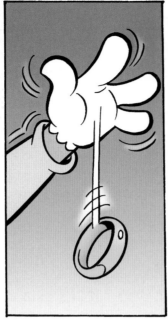

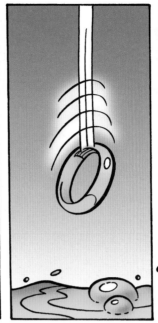

THE STINKY GAME!

This game is brilliant at parties!

1 Get a grown-up to help you find as many smelly things as you can.

2 Now pop the pongy things in a bag and invite your friends over for a game!

3 Get your friends to close their eyes. They have to guess what they are smelling as you wave each thing under their noses.

47

TOM & JERRY

DANGEROUS GARDEN

Hey, Tom, ol' buddy! What's going on? Why the long face?

As a cat I'm a failure! You know what Jerry did while I was out? He went and bought some plants for the garden!

Is that all? Why don't we go in there and stomp them into the dirt? Like this! Look!

It's not as easy as that! Come on and I'll show you why!

They're meat eating plants and he's got them all trained!

Gulp!

END

chocolate

ice cream

mousse

fruit cake

sorbet

Swiss roll

FULL OF GOODNESS
Written and drawn by Oscar Martin

Look at all those cakes, Tuffy!

Yuck! Give me cheese any day!

Hmm. You've just given me an idea how to get some extra money!

Later...

Hee-hee! I told you my plan would work!

You're so smart, Jerry!

I'll have one too!

Easy, guys, there's enough for everyone!

Cheesecake

Cheese ice cream

Cheese mousse

SNOWMEN BEWARE!

Written and drawn by Oscar Martin

BIFF!

Eee-ouch!

CRACK

Grrr!

You see Tuffy? When water freezes hard enough, you can walk on it! Cool, huh?

I'll get them now!

Uh-oh!

Hey, what's happening? Is someone pulling me backwards?

CRASH!

Ha! He should have studied physics! He didn't think about his weight on the ice!

What a headache! I'm not feeling very well!

WHAAAT!?

All this is their fault!

One big flattened snowman coming up!

Say goodbye to your snowman, guys! Hee-hee-hee!

CLANG

Look, he fell for it! How can anyone be that dumb? Ha ha ha!

Ha Ha!